BEETHOVEN

Andante Favori for Pianoforte

WoO 57

Edited and annotated by

HOWARD FERGUSON

THE ASSOCIATED BOARD OF
THE ROYAL SCHOOLS OF MUSIC

INTRODUCTION

The *Andante Favori* was written during 1803-4 as the slow movement of the Sonata in C, Op.53, popularly known as the 'Waldstein'. But when Beethoven played the work from the manuscript to some of his friends, it was suggested that the *Andante* made it too long. At first he indignantly denied this; soon, however, he came to realize that not only was it too long, but that it was in an earlier and far less sophisticated style than the rest. He therefore substituted the short but profoundly moving *Introduzione* that now provides the Sonata's slow movement, and allowed the *Andante* to be published as a separate work a year later.

The present text follows the 1st edition: *Andante pour le Pianoforte composé par Louis van Beethoven*; Bureau des Arts et d'Industrie, Vienna [1806], plate No.506.*(The word *Favori* was added to the title in later editions.) The fingering throughout is editorial, and so are slurs crossed with a small vertical stroke. Other editorial additions are printed either within square brackets or in small type. A suggested metronome mark will be found below the final bar. It should be remembered, however, that it is neither authoritative nor binding.

My thanks are due to the British Library Board for allowing access to a copy of the 1st edition, and for giving permission for its use in preparing the present text.

HOWARD FERGUSON
Cambridge 1983

*The autograph has not survived.

ANDANTE FAVORI
WoO 57

BEETHOVEN

Andante grazioso con moto

(a)

(b) Beethoven's *cresc.* . . . *p implies* a *cresc.* followed by a sudden drop to *p*.

(c)

AB 1852

1) B. 47, r.h.: there are no triplet-signs in the source, but presumably triplets were intended.

2) B.103: in the source the *sfp* is on the 2nd quaver; but the position shown seems more probable.

AB 1852

3) B.147: the second *p* is surprising. Probably it was copied mistakenly from the previous bar.

Printed in England by Caligraving Limited Thetford Norfolk

AB 1852

2:95